Pat Sajak

GAMES & Puzzles

FEATURING PAT'S PATENT PENDING CODE LETTER™ SCRAMBLES

Use the Code Letter icons to help unscramble the mixed-up letters to spell common words.

HOW DO YOU RANK?

Zero completed = F	Six completed = B+
One or two completed = D	Seven completed = A-
Three or four completed = C	Eight completed = A
Five completed = B	Nine completed = A+

ANSWERS: Each puzzle is numbered. Answers are located at the back of the book.

Dalmatian Press

Printed in Ft. Wayne, IN, U.S.A.
The **DALMATIAN PRESS** name and logo are trademarks of Dalmatian Publishing Group, Franklin, TN 37067. 1-866-418-2572.

CE14372/0811

PAT SAJAK'S

GAMES & Puzzles

#1

FEATURING PAT'S PATENT PENDING

CODE LETTER SCRAMBLES

INSTRUCTIONS:
The code icons help identify letters in these mixed-up common words. Once you figure out a Code Letter, write the letter in each coded square of the 9 words.

NOUIN

#1

U	N	I	O	N

DYELO

#2

Y	O	D	E	L

LOWEH

#3

W	H	O	L	E

YRDBIH

#4

H	Y	B	R	I	D

HBEROT

#5

B	O	T	H	E	R

CBFIRA

#6

		B			

LHUILP

#7

		H		L	L

TLEESN

#8

N			T	L	

BARDVE

#9

					B

PAT SAJAK'S

GAMES & Puzzles #2

FEATURING PAT'S PATENT PENDING

CODE LETTER SCRAMBLES

STPNA

#1

UEBSL

#2

PTRBUA

#3

UONATM

#4

DLBEIR

#5

AECMAR

#6

NGRJOA

#7

HECNSO

#8

GEMANL

#9

PAT SAJAK'S

GAMES & Puzzles #3

FEATURING PAT'S PATENT PENDING

CODE LETTER SCRAMBLES

ATDIL

#1 ☐ ☐ ☐□ ☐ ☐△

DKOAV

#2 ☐☆ ☐ ☐ ☐ ☐

LEFMU

#3 ☐◇ ☐△ ☐ ☐ ☐

AEVINT

#4 ☐(maple leaf) ☐ ☐ ☐□ ☐☆ ☐

BTRTIE

#5 ☐ ☐□ ☐ ☐ ☐ ☐

YISLMF

#6 ☐◇ ☐△ ☐□ ☐ ☐○ ☐

ALUTCA

#7 ☐ ☐ ☐ ☐ ☐ ☐△

TOMSCA

#8 ☐ ☐ ☐○ ☐ ☐ ☐

AETNCO

#9 ☐ ☐ ☐ ☐ ☐(maple leaf) ☐

PAT SAJAK'S

GAMES & Puzzles #4

FEATURING PAT'S PATENT PENDING

CODE LETTER SCRAMBLES

#1 NWNKO

	♧	☆		♧

#2 UASBC

□		△	◇	

#3 ROMNO

⊛	☆		☆	♧

#4 LMAORN

♧	☆		⊛		

#5 TMSIFI

⊛		□			

#6 RYLRBU

◇		△			

#7 TATUNM

⊛	△			♧	

#8 PEURMJ

	△	⊛			

#9 ASLOTP

	☆	□			

PAT SAJAK'S

GAMES & Puzzles

5

FEATURING PAT'S PATENT PENDING

CODE LETTER SCRAMBLES

OAGCR

#1 ◇ _ _ ♧ _

GANCO

#2 ◇ _ _ ♧ _

NAPTL

#3 □ _ _ _ 🍁

VNARTE

#4 🍁 _ _ _ _ _

EMLIPP

#5 □ ☆ _ □ _ _

ECLHNC

#6 ◇ _ _ _ ◇ _

PAILCD

#7 □ _ _ ◇ ☆ _

AISRIN

#8 _ _ ☆ _ ☆ _

TOCEKP

#9 □ _ ◇ _ _ 🍁

PAT SAJAK'S

GAMES & Puzzles #6

FEATURING PAT'S PATENT PENDING

CODE LETTER SCRAMBLES

EURGP

#1 ☐♣ ☐ ☐ ☐ ☐

YKRPE

#2 ☐♣ ☐ ☐ ☐ ☐⊛

HATCL

#3 ☐ ☐ ☐ ☐☆ ☐✤

DORWAC

#4 ☐☆ ☐□ ☐ ☐ ☐ ☐

YLJPAO

#5 ☐ ☐ ☐ ☐□ ☐♣ ☐⊛

NVSHAI

#6 ☐ ☐ ☐ ☐ ☐ ☐✤

YUHPCN

#7 ☐♣ ☐ ☐ ☐☆ ☐✤ ☐⊛

RECPEY

#8 ☐☆ ☐ ☐ ☐ ☐♣ ☐⊛

TAOTOP

#9 ☐♣ ☐□ ☐ ☐ ☐ ☐□

PAT SAJAK'S

GAMES & Puzzles #7

FEATURING PAT'S PATENT PENDING

CODE LETTER SCRAMBLES

KESNNU

#1

ITVIMC

#2

TAGUEO

#3

NIPCCI

#4

NSGVIA

#5

TESFYA

#6

AECBNO

#7

UMAOTN

#8

HSKRNU

#9

PAT SAJAK'S

GAMES & Puzzles #8

FEATURING PAT'S PATENT PENDING

CODE LETTER SCRAMBLES

ULAOD

#1 ☐ ☐△ ☐☆ ☐ ☐

URMLE

#2 ☐△ ☐ ☐◇ ☐ ☐

RMUBC

#3 ☐ ☐ ☐ ☐◇ ☐

UYPMGR

#4 ☐□ ☐ ☐ ☐◇ ☐ ☐

TFUHGO

#5 ☐ ☐☆ ☐ ☐□ ☐♧ ☐🍁

NETXET

#6 ☐ ☐ ☐🍁 ☐ ☐⊛ ☐🍁

ENCRHI

#7 ☐ ☐⊛ ☐ ☐ ☐ ☐♧

NPPHEA

#8 ☐♧ ☐ ☐ ☐ ☐ ☐⊛

RSHGUE

#9 ☐□ ☐ ☐ ☐♧ ☐ ☐

PAT SAJAK'S

GAMES & Puzzles #9

FEATURING PAT'S PATENT PENDING

CODE LETTER SCRAMBLES

#1 TRAMKE

◇					

#2 TGMUNE

	△		◇		□

#3 ATEGOU

	△			□	

#4 RROBHA

♧					

#5 PEHPRO

♧					

#6 UDNFRE

		🍁	△		

#7 EEMLHT

♧			◇		

#8 SUEFRE

		🍁	△		

#9 HLBREA

♧					

PAT SAJAK'S

GAMES & Puzzles #10

FEATURING PAT'S PATENT PENDING

CODE LETTER SCRAMBLES

GETAEN

#1 ☐ ☐☆ ☐ ☐ ☐ ☐☆

VWLSIE

#2 ☐ ☐ ☐ ☐◇ ☐☆ ☐

RBRBEA

#3 ☐ ☐ ☐ ☐ ☐☆ ☐

NEOJID

#4 ☐ ☐ ☐ ☐ ☐☆ ☐⊛

RVEONG

#5 ☐ ☐ ☐◇ ☐☆ ☐ ☐

EIETPT

#6 ☐○ ☐☆ ☐ ☐ ☐ ☐☆

SUTDNI

#7 ☐ ☐ ☐⊛ ☐ ☐ ☐

GEPTIL

#8 ☐○ ☐ ☐ ☐ ☐☆ ☐

RPNOES

#9 ☐○ ☐☆ ☐ ☐ ☐ ☐

PAT SAJAK'S

GAMES & Puzzles #11

FEATURING PAT'S PATENT PENDING

CODE LETTER SCRAMBLES

EPRPUL

#1

♧		△	♧	□	◇

BIPOAH

#2

♧		☆			

DORINO

#3

	⊛		☆	☆	△

ETDECI

#4

	◇		◇		

MBTUEL

#5

				□	◇

RTATNY

#6

		△		⊛	

LWAPLO

#7

		□	□	☆	♧

TEDFAE

#8

	◇		◇		

BVRLAE

#9

	◇	△			□

PAT SAJAK'S

GAMES & Puzzles #12

FEATURING PAT'S PATENT PENDING

CODE LETTER SCRAMBLES

BANDPE

#1

SESSAS

#2

TADYIN

#3

YIFRUT

#4

FIFMUN

#5

USJOOY

#6

EQUSAY

#7

WUNDIN

#8

ZZANYS

#9

PAT SAJAK'S

GAMES & Puzzles #13

FEATURING PAT'S PATENT PENDING

CODE LETTER SCRAMBLES

ELRCYE

#1

◇				♧	☆

OCULKN

#2

				◇	△

GHRONT

#3

♡	○	♧			

AMUDIR

#4

♧					

TTALET

#5

♡		♡	♡		

RYHERS

#6

	○		♧	♧	☆

CELOOT

#7

	◇				♡

TWKICE

#8

		◇	△		♡

HYROTN

#9

♡	○		♧		☆

PAT SAJAK'S

GAMES & Puzzles #14

FEATURING PAT'S PATENT PENDING

CODE LETTER SCRAMBLES

TYIMSC

#1

☆		◇			🍁

SLIALE

#2

	□	□			◇

PARCHO

#3

🍁					△

BYOPIS

#4

⊛			△	◇	

GACCON

#5

🍁		♧			🍁

MOBLAP

#6

	△	□		☆	⊛

GLUBEN

#7

⊛			♧	□	

FLUNGE

#8

		♧		□	

ABAMOE

#9

	☆			⊛	

PAT SAJAK'S

GAMES & Puzzles #15

FEATURING PAT'S PATENT PENDING

CODE LETTER SCRAMBLES

LOBGGE

#1

	△	☆	☆		

INGUMP

#2

			♧	☆	

GRIFTH

#3

	🍁		☆	◇	

GHOUFT

#4

	△	♧	☆	◇	

WARMOR

#5

		🍁	🍁	△	

THKING

#6

♡			☆	◇	

DAGGEG

#7

☆		☆	☆		

GROOFE

#8

	△	🍁		☆	△

HERACK

#9

◇			♡		🍁

PAT SAJAK'S

GAMES & Puzzles #16

FEATURING PAT'S PATENT PENDING

CODE LETTER SCRAMBLES

DRABER

#1 | | ○ | | ♡ | ♡ | | △ |

CYLEER

#2 | | | | □ | | ♡ | |

TANKEL

#3 | | | | ☆ | □ | | |

KEIBOO

#4 | | ○ | | | ☆ | | |

GRAYCG

#5 | | | ♡ | | | | |

MORRED

#6 | | △ | | ♡ | | | ♡ |

WAKNEA

#7 | | | | | ☆ | | |

BIBBON

#8 | | ○ | | ○ | ○ | | |

CLODDE

#9 | | | | △ | △ | □ | |

PAT SAJAK'S

GAMES & Puzzles

17

FEATURING PAT'S PATENT PENDING

CODE LETTER SCRAMBLES

DETODT

#1

ICTAIL

#2

SIFTEY

#3

LYHGIH

#4

DINALN

#5

WAGFUF

#6

LYNVEE

#7

JILREA

#8

ZIFYRZ

#9

PAT SAJAK'S

GAMES & Puzzles #18

FEATURING PAT'S PATENT PENDING

CODE LETTER SCRAMBLES

MUHEAN

#1 ☐ ☐ ☐ ☐ ☐ ☐ (□ on 1, ♡ on 3, ○ on 4)

ROQUIL

#2 ☐ ☐ ☐ ☐ ☐ ☐ (♣ on 1, ☆ on 6)

KILGIN

#3 ☐ ☐ ☐ ☐ ☐ ☐ (♣ on 1)

TELTEM

#4 ☐ ☐ ☐ ☐ ☐ ☐ (♡ on 1, ♣ on 5)

TSASIE

#5 ☐ ☐ ☐ ☐ ☐ ☐ (△ on 1, △ on 4, ○ on 6)

CAPERN

#6 ☐ ☐ ☐ ☐ ☐ ☐ (☆ on 2, ○ on 3)

REOTMN

#7 ☐ ☐ ☐ ☐ ☐ ☐ (♡ on 1, ☆ on 6)

SHUDHE

#8 ☐ ☐ ☐ ☐ ☐ ☐ (□ on 1, △ on 3, □ on 4)

JUSTIR

#9 ☐ ☐ ☐ ☐ ☐ ☐ (☆ on 3, △ on 5)

PAT SAJAK'S

GAMES & Puzzles #19

FEATURING PAT'S PATENT PENDING

CODE LETTER SCRAMBLES

MENTGU

#1 | | ♧ | | | | ☆ |

AONECT

#2 | | ♡ | | | | |

LPREUP

#3 | | ♧ | | | ◇ | |

RUMEES

#4 | | | | ♧ | | |

ZGBOEA

#5 | ☆ | | | | | |

GRITFH

#6 | | | | ☆ | △ | |

TFUHOR

#7 | | | ♧ | | | △ |

CURHNC

#8 | ♡ | | ♧ | | ♡ | △ |

LDPYEO

#9 | | | | ◇ | | |

PAT SAJAK'S

GAMES & Puzzles #20

FEATURING PAT'S PATENT PENDING

CODE LETTER SCRAMBLES

ADUELL

#1 [ ][△][△][ ][ ][ ]

CRABKE

#2 [ ][ ][♡][◇][ ][ ]

PANTAC

#3 [♡][ ][ ][ ][ ][♧]

CLAKCE

#4 [♡][ ][♡][◇][△][ ]

CHINFL

#5 [ ][△][ ][ ][♡][ ]

UTRIPY

#6 [♧][ ][ ][ ][ ][□]

GRINCY

#7 [♡][ ][□][ ][ ][☆]

VARGLE

#8 [☆][ ][ ][ ][ ][△]

LIELOC

#9 [♡][ ][△][△][ ][ ]

PAT SAJAK'S

GAMES & Puzzles # 21

FEATURING PAT'S PATENT PENDING

CODE LETTER SCRAMBLES

SHIVAR

#1 ☐○ ☐ ☐ ☐ ☐ ☐☆

CLYKUP

#2 ☐□ ☐ ☐ ☐♣ ☐ ☐

TRHOWN

#3 ☐ ☐☆ ☐○ ☐ ☐♣ ☐

FINCET

#4 ☐ ☐ ☐ ☐ ☐♣ ☐

VINGGI

#5 ☐♡ ☐ ☐ ☐ ☐ ☐♡

PLOYJA

#6 ☐ ☐ ☐ ☐ ☐□ ☐

GIRRED

#7 ☐♡ ☐ ☐○ ☐ ☐ ☐○

OWNNER

#8 ☐○ ☐ ☐ ☐ ☐♣ ☐

SOCCAT

#9 ☐ ☐♣ ☐♣ ☐ ☐ ☐

PAT SAJAK'S

GAMES & Puzzles #22

FEATURING PAT'S PATENT PENDING

CODE LETTER SCRAMBLES

PTUPEP

#1

CLIPES

#2

DORUSH

#3

DATTEM

#4

TROVEL

#5

SLOMAN

#6

HAPNOR

#7

ROMMIE

#8

EMBRIL

#9

PAT SAJAK'S

GAMES & Puzzles #23

FEATURING PAT'S PATENT PENDING

CODE LETTER SCRAMBLES

DAHERC

#1

♡					☆

WIEHTN

#2

△			□		

BYRWNA

#3

♧		♡	△		

OWENOD

#4

△			☆		

PRMCEA

#5

	♡				

ZBRUZE

#6

♧					

OPITTE

#7

□			□		

REUDAG

#8

♡					☆

TIHRWE

#9

△		□			

PAT SAJAK'S

GAMES & Puzzles #24

FEATURING PAT'S PATENT PENDING

CODE LETTER SCRAMBLES

CHADTE

#1

○			♧	🍁	

OGRUBE

#2

	☆		♡		

CARFAS

#3

	☆	♧	🍁	♧	

HUCCOR

#4

🍁	☆			🍁	

PEARME

#5

♧				☆	

GLYCER

#6

🍁			☆	♡	

VATIEA

#7

♧			♧		

DICERN

#8

🍁			○		☆

STIDVE

#9

○					

PAT SAJAK'S

GAMES & Puzzles # 25

FEATURING PAT'S PATENT PENDING

CODE LETTER SCRAMBLES

EMTRON

#1 ◇ ♧

RSMQUI

#2 □ ◇

WRYIEN

#3 ♧

MOATUN

#4 ◇ ♧

NOOSAL

#5 □ ♧

USPURM

#6 ◇ □

LETDEM

#7 ◇ ☆

SABMAL

#8 □ ◇

CEDUSE

#9 □ ☆

PAT SAJAK'S

GAMES & Puzzles #26

FEATURING PAT'S PATENT PENDING

CODE LETTER SCRAMBLES

VERPON

#1

☆					

EZEHEW

#2

△					

LIMPPE

#3

☆			☆		

EPOUTE

#4

♧			☆		

PSOPAE

#5

	☆	☆			

INNPET

#6

♧			☆		

YAAPPA

#7

☆		☆			

CTHREW

#8

△			♧		

YANYAW

#9

			△		

PAT SAJAK'S

GAMES & Puzzles #27

FEATURING PAT'S PATENT PENDING

CODE LETTER SCRAMBLES

RHBIYD

#1 ☐☐☐☐☐☐

YALDIV

#2 ☐☐☐☐☐☐

YOSUBB

#3 ☐☐☐☐☐☐

NOYANE

#4 ☐☐☐☐☐☐

AMAGED

#5 ☐☐☐☐☐☐

YAPADY

#6 ☐☐☐☐☐☐

YOPLED

#7 ☐☐☐☐☐☐

RAFODF

#8 ☐☐☐☐☐☐

GANEYC

#9 ☐☐☐☐☐☐

PAT SAJAK'S

GAMES & Puzzles #28

FEATURING PAT'S PATENT PENDING

CODE LETTER SCRAMBLES

#1 A E H N G C

□	♡				

#2 M B O E E C

		□	◇	☆	

#3 D O W N O E

	◇	◇	♧		

#4 D O R A M N

			♧	◇	☆

#5 N L E Y O L

	◇				△

#6 B S A Y B H

	♡				△

#7 A Y N C K R

□					△

#8 R O A U D N

		◇			♧

#9 H B C U Y B

□	♡				△

PAT SAJAK'S

GAMES & Puzzles #29

FEATURING PAT'S PATENT PENDING

CODE LETTER SCRAMBLES

GTNEHL

#1

		♡	□		☆

UMNRBE

#2

♡		△	◇		

RLSOLC

#3

	♧				

ULHMBE

#4

☆		△	◇		

AHOSWD

#5

	☆				

AGLONO

#6

		□			♡

MHIETR

#7

☆			△		

GLYCAE

#8

		□		♧	

CNIEVO

#9

♡				♧	

PAT SAJAK'S

GAMES & Puzzles #30

FEATURING PAT'S PATENT PENDING

CODE LETTER SCRAMBLES

ELWEYK

#1 [ ][ ][♣][♣][☆][ ][△]

TRSSES

#2 [ ][ ][ ][♣][ ][ ]

DLUYOL

#3 [ ][ ][ ][ ][ ][△]

EKLCRO

#4 [ ][ ][ ][☆][♣][ ]

TEPYTR

#5 [ ][ ][♣][ ][ ][△]

ECYPHA

#6 [ ][♣][ ][ ][ ][△]

LEALYG

#7 [ ][ ][ ][ ][♣][△]

TNIEMT

#8 [ ][ ][ ][ ][♣][ ]

YMIFLA

#9 [ ][ ][ ][ ][ ][△]

PAT SAJAK'S

GAMES & Puzzles #31

FEATURING PAT'S PATENT PENDING

CODE LETTER SCRAMBLES

RARBLE

#1

	△			◇	

MRPETI

#2

	◇				

FIOTTU

#3

			♧		

RCHHUC

#4

☆				☆	

ECVRLE

#5

☆		◇		◇	

TRLETE

#6

	◇			◇	

ARFLMO

#7

♧				△	

CLDOEK

#8

		☆		◇	

LROELR

#9

				◇	

PAT SAJAK'S

GAMES & Puzzles #32

FEATURING PAT'S PATENT PENDING

CODE LETTER SCRAMBLES

TARLUB

#1 | ♣ | | △ | | | ☆ |

TRUGET

#2 | □ | △ | | | | |

GEEALB

#3 | ♣ | | | □ | ☆ | |

NOSELS

#4 | ☆ | | | | | |

TIBNAD

#5 | ♣ | | | | | |

AKCALJ

#6 | | | | | | ☆ |

GILPET

#7 | | | □ | ☆ | | |

BURREB

#8 | | △ | ♣ | ♣ | | |

LEZIFZ

#9 | | | | | ☆ | |

PAT SAJAK'S

GAMES & Puzzles #33

FEATURING PAT'S PATENT PENDING

CODE LETTER SCRAMBLES

SNOPER

#1 ☐ ☐◇ ☐ ☐ ☐○ ☐

IEIVDD

#2 ☐ ☐ ☐ ☐ ☐ ☐◇

COUTNA

#3 ☐ ☐○ ☐ ☐ ☐ ☐

PREYSO

#4 ☐○ ☐ ☐ ☐ ☐◇ ☐

PALGOL

#5 ☐ ☐ ☐ ☐ ☐○ ☐

REPPPE

#6 ☐ ☐◇ ☐ ☐ ☐◇ ☐

TYCOOE

#7 ☐ ☐○ ☐ ☐○ ☐ ☐◇

SSSERT

#8 ☐ ☐ ☐ ☐◇ ☐ ☐

HOSECO

#9 ☐ ☐ ☐○ ☐○ ☐ ☐◇

PAT SAJAK'S

GAMES & Puzzles #34

FEATURING PAT'S PATENT PENDING

CODE LETTER SCRAMBLES

YERTAT

#1 ☐☐☐☐☐☐ (6th box: maple leaf)

GINILV

#2 ☐☐☐☐☐☐ (3rd box: ☆, 5th box: □)

CHENWR

#3 ☐☐☐☐☐☐ (4th box: □, 6th box: △)

HOEDMT

#4 ☐☐☐☐☐☐ (4th box: △, 6th box: ◇)

ADBETE

#5 ☐☐☐☐☐☐ (1st box: ◇)

VRAEBE

#6 ☐☐☐☐☐☐ (4th box: ☆)

RHYETO

#7 ☐☐☐☐☐☐ (2nd box: △, 6th box: maple leaf)

NIVERD

#8 ☐☐☐☐☐☐ (1st box: ◇, 4th box: ☆, 6th box: □)

HISDLE

#9 ☐☐☐☐☐☐ (2nd box: △, 6th box: ◇)

PAT SAJAK'S

GAMES & Puzzles #35

FEATURING PAT'S PATENT PENDING

CODE LETTER SCRAMBLES

#1 PARBUT

				☆	

#2 LOAFRM

♡					⊛

#3 CATROF

♡		♧			

#4 SEALWE

🍁					⊛

#5 DRAILZ

⊛					

#6 LOOPAL

	☆		⊛	⊛	

#7 SURLAW

🍁		⊛			

#8 HENCAC

♧				♧	

#9 SAUTEL

		⊛			

PAT SAJAK'S

GAMES & Puzzles #36

FEATURING PAT'S PATENT PENDING

CODE LETTER SCRAMBLES

FETEDC

#1 | | | ⊛ | | △ | |

VINEDA

#2 | | | | □ | | |

CBBOTA

#3 | | | | △ | □ | |

YOMKEN

#4 | | | | | | ♡ |

IFHISN

#5 | ⊛ | | | | | |

ARGAEG

#6 | | □ | | □ | | |

CAKEBD

#7 | | □ | △ | | | |

RKYUET

#8 | | ♧ | | | | ♡ |

ELBUBB

#9 | | ♧ | | | | |

PAT SAJAK'S

GAMES & Puzzles #37

FEATURING PAT'S PATENT PENDING

CODE LETTER SCRAMBLES

HEALGG

#1 | | | | | |

PUTSID

#2 | | | | | |

TINEIF

#3 | | | | | |

BITBAR

#4 | | | | | |

ACETKJ

#5 | | | | | |

COVENX

#6 | | | | | |

LATEBL

#7 | | | | | |

HEMCES

#8 | | | | | |

LATUAC

#9 | | | | | |

PAT SAJAK'S

GAMES & Puzzles #38

FEATURING PAT'S PATENT PENDING

CODE LETTER SCRAMBLES

RISKHN

#1

	♣		△		♡

WOOLHL

#2

♣	○			○	

BAVEEH

#3

□		♣			

FLABFE

#4

□					

ETELKT

#5

♡					

ZLOZEN

#6

	○				

GAMINK

#7

		♡	△		

THIRFG

#8

		△		♣	

GTHNIK

#9

♡		△		♣	

PAT SAJAK'S

GAMES & Puzzles #39

FEATURING PAT'S PATENT PENDING

CODE LETTER SCRAMBLES

EEZREF

#1 | △ | | | | | |

FLARET

#2 | △ | ♧ | | ☆ | | |

GUMSED

#3 | | ◇ | | ○ | | |

GLEPED

#4 | ♡ | | | ○ | | |

TOREMH

#5 | ◇ | | ☆ | | | |

PANNIK

#6 | | ♧ | ♡ | | | |

LOLMEW

#7 | ◇ | | | | | |

MBCATO

#8 | | | ◇ | | ♧ | ☆ |

ANONNC

#9 | | ♧ | | | | |

PAT SAJAK'S

GAMES & Puzzles #40

FEATURING PAT'S PATENT PENDING

CODE LETTER SCRAMBLES

SOOUYJ

#1

		□			

CHAING

#2

	☆	◇		△	

KATCAT

#3

				☆	

MHEARM

#4

◇				○	

OFMATH

#5

			◇		

CLUEDD

#6

☆					○

LCOIEP

#7

				☆	○

FISHYT

#8

	◇				□

NOTACI

#9

	☆				△

PAT SAJAK'S

GAMES & Puzzles

41

FEATURING PAT'S PATENT PENDING

CODE LETTER SCRAMBLES

UYDOLC

#1 ☆ at box 1, ○ at box 4

☆			○		

MUSNOM

#2

	○				

CAMPTI

#3

△		◇		☆	♧

MDIEPE

#4

△		◇			

WUDNIN

#5

○			△		

NCETRH

#6

♧				☆	

RUMSTE

#7

	○		♧		

PHULIL

#8

○	◇		△		

NORHAP

#9

		◇			

PAT SAJAK'S

GAMES & Puzzles #42

FEATURING PAT'S PATENT PENDING

CODE LETTER SCRAMBLES

FATEED

#1 | | △ | | △ | ♧ | |

EONYAN

#2 | ♧ | | | ♡ | | △ |

CAPETC

#3 | ♧ | | | △ | | |

VIETIN

#4 | ☆ | | | ☆ | | △ |

JETCOB

#5 | ♡ | | | △ | | |

GNIMIN

#6 | | ☆ | | ☆ | | |

DFONEF

#7 | ♡ | | | △ | | |

SLUNES

#8 | | | | △ | | |

CESXES

#9 | △ | | | △ | | |

PAT SAJAK'S

GAMES & Puzzles #43

FEATURING PAT'S PATENT PENDING

CODE LETTER SCRAMBLES

RUNJYI

#1

	♡				□

CUESAC

#2

				○	

DROAWN

#3

	♡	♣			

GTIEIN

#4

		♡		☆	

UACTSC

#5

			☆		○

EENUNV

#6

	♡				♡

WSLAYA

#7

		♣		□	○

NEATOC

#8

		☆		♡	

GLOBON

#9

				♡	

PAT SAJAK'S

GAMES & Puzzles #44

FEATURING PAT'S PATENT PENDING

CODE LETTER SCRAMBLES

SUMSSI

#1

PEARME

#2

JOYPAL

#3

ROAMWR

#4

CREAMP

#5

PLUMCY

#6

UNSLIM

#7

CHUPYN

#8

PURSUM

#9

PAT SAJAK'S

GAMES & Puzzles #45

FEATURING PAT'S PATENT PENDING

CODE LETTER SCRAMBLES

MISURQ

#1

RAIDOT

#2

WARLYC

#3

TEAQUE

#4

LEESQU

#5

IBIDTT

#6

QUIBSE

#7

TANSCY

#8

CUTBAD

#9

PAT SAJAK'S

GAMES & Puzzles #46

FEATURING PAT'S PATENT PENDING

CODE LETTER SCRAMBLES

TERMKA

#1 | | | ○ | ♡ | | |

TELANK

#2 | | | ♡ | | | |

YKLARD

#3 | | | ○ | ♡ | | |

ARCHKE

#4 | | | | ♡ | | ○ |

RSAVEE

#5 | | | | ○ | ♣ | |

LIKERL

#6 | ♡ | | | | | ○ |

RAKEUE

#7 | | | ○ | | ♡ | |

CRIBEK

#8 | | | | ♡ | | ○ |

RUSKNH

#9 | ♣ | | ○ | | | ♡ |

PAT SAJAK'S

GAMES & Puzzles

#47

FEATURING PAT'S PATENT PENDING

CODE LETTER SCRAMBLES

PLOTEP

#1

ARTYRO

#2

HAILTW

#3

GRONTH

#4

SFYEAT

#5

MISTYE

#6

LOUTDN

#7

SAXYNT

#8

REWNYI

#9

PAT SAJAK'S

GAMES & Puzzles

48

FEATURING PAT'S PATENT PENDING

CODE LETTER SCRAMBLES

SAGEDO

#1 | | | | | | |

RAGELY

#2 | | | | | | |

ROVEDU

#3 | | | | | | |

RAILBT

#4 | | | | | | |

YINTAD

#5 | | | | | | |

PBSYIO

#6 | | | | | | |

ACERHB

#7 | | | | | | |

LUNGEF

#8 | | | | | | |

GRINIW

#9 | | | | | | |

PAT SAJAK'S

GAMES & Puzzles #49

FEATURING PAT'S PATENT PENDING

CODE LETTER SCRAMBLES

FCOINF

#1

AILCAF

#2

CABNOE

#3

FCEETD

#4

SIFYKR

#5

HISFYT

#6

TIESBC

#7

OKIEOC

#8

THINCE

#9

PAT SAJAK'S

GAMES & Puzzles #50

FEATURING PAT'S PATENT PENDING

CODE LETTER SCRAMBLES

#1 REGRUB

#2 POLHAO

#3 DEALSD

#4 SLOTPA

#5 CHINFL

#6 FLEARO

#7 GINDIT

#8 MOBPAL

#9 DUELSG

PAT SAJAK'S

GAMES & Puzzles #51

FEATURING PAT'S PATENT PENDING

CODE LETTER SCRAMBLES

LUANAN

#1 ☐☐☐☐☐☐ (6th letter ⊛)

CENFED

#2 ☐☐☐☐☐☐ (2nd letter ♡, 4th letter ◇)

CHABLN

#3 ☐☐☐☐☐☐ (1st letter ♧, 2nd letter ⊛, 5th letter ◇)

PROACH

#4 ☐☐☐☐☐☐ (1st letter ◇, 5th letter ☆, 6th letter ○)

PCYLUM

#5 ☐☐☐☐☐☐ (1st letter ◇, 2nd letter ⊛, 5th letter ○)

FLEDTY

#6 ☐☐☐☐☐☐ (3rd letter ♡, 5th letter ⊛)

ROBELO

#7 ☐☐☐☐☐☐ (1st letter ♧, 2nd letter ☆, 3rd letter ⊛, 6th letter ☆)

FEMALA

#8 ☐☐☐☐☐☐ (2nd letter ♡, 3rd letter ⊛)

PEARMC

#9 ☐☐☐☐☐☐ (1st letter ◇, 4th letter ○)

PAT SAJAK'S

GAMES & Puzzles #52

FEATURING PAT'S PATENT PENDING

CODE LETTER SCRAMBLES

CARESE

#1 ☐☆ ☐ ☐ ☐⊛ ☐ ☐

COBYUN

#2 ☐ ☐ ☐ ☐△ ☐☆ ☐♣

NERUSE

#3 ☐ ☐△ ☐ ☐ ☐ ☐

YARDFT

#4 ☐◇ ☐ ☐⊛ ☐ ☐ ☐♣

LGEAGH

#5 ☐ ☐⊛ ☐♡ ☐♡ ☐ ☐

CHARDE

#6 ☐⊛ ☐ ☐☆ ☐ ☐ ☐◇

RYEINW

#7 ☐ ☐ ☐△ ☐ ☐ ☐♣

CARTOV

#8 ☐☆ ☐⊛ ☐ ☐ ☐ ☐

YARING

#9 ☐♡ ☐ ☐⊛ ☐ ☐△ ☐♣

PAT SAJAK'S

GAMES & Puzzles #53

FEATURING PAT'S PATENT PENDING

CODE LETTER SCRAMBLES

REALIJ

#1 | | | △ | ☆ | | |

SEUEDC

#2 | | | ♧ | | ○ | |

GAMIEP

#3 | | | ✤ | ♡ | △ | |

SEEPOD

#4 | ♧ | | ♡ | | | |

CXLIMA

#5 | ○ | ☆ | △ | | | |

CREAPN

#6 | ♡ | | | | ○ | |

NALDIN

#7 | △ | | ☆ | | | ♧ |

BUADTC

#8 | | | ♧ | | ○ | |

SENTEL

#9 | | | | | ☆ | |

PAT SAJAK'S

GAMES & Puzzles #54

FEATURING PAT'S PATENT PENDING

CODE LETTER SCRAMBLES

TIDESV

#1

RUBECH

#2

GOLUSH

#3

STUNDI

#4

BLAREH

#5

MADRUI

#6

PACTEU

#7

VEERDI

#8

DOKWRE

#9

PAT SAJAK'S

GAMES & Puzzles #55

FEATURING PAT'S PATENT PENDING

CODE LETTER SCRAMBLES

RCHDAE

#1 | | | | | |

TURFIY

#2 | | | | | |

SQUIBE

#3 | | | | | |

DREAMK

#4 | | | | | |

SCULLA

#5 | | | | | |

BOPALM

#6 | | | | | |

YANKSE

#7 | | | | | |

CHALKE

#8 | | | | | |

KSIMEO

#9 | | | | | |

PAT SAJAK'S

GAMES & Puzzles #56

FEATURING PAT'S PATENT PENDING

CODE LETTER SCRAMBLES

ERROCG

#1

AFGULR

#2

BLRIEM

#3

DLBIER

#4

CEMBOE

#5

NEELKN

#6

DRCEUS

#7

TEDILA

#8

RNOIMF

#9

PAT SAJAK'S

GAMES & Puzzles #57

FEATURING PAT'S PATENT PENDING

CODE LETTER SCRAMBLES

EGRME

#1

LILYH

#2

OGVRE

#3

EHXAEL

#4

HGARAN

#5

VEAGLR

#6

VILAUS

#7

UTOHRF

#8

ZEOABG

#9

PAT SAJAK'S

GAMES & Puzzles #58

FEATURING PAT'S PATENT PENDING

CODE LETTER SCRAMBLES

LAAHP

#1 | | | | ○ | |

RHDOA

#2 | ○ | ⊛ | | | |

ACOLL

#3 | | ⊛ | ♧ | | |

HGWITE

#4 | ◇ | ☆ | | | ○ | |

LEFKCI

#5 | | | ♧ | | | ☆ |

GESVAA

#6 | | | | | | ☆ |

WRINIG

#7 | ◇ | | | | | |

CNHREW

#8 | ◇ | | ☆ | | ♧ | ○ |

AWAYIR

#9 | | | | ◇ | | |

PAT SAJAK'S

GAMES & Puzzles

#59

FEATURING PAT'S PATENT PENDING

CODE LETTER SCRAMBLES

SRUVES

#1 [ ][ ][ ][ ][ ][ ] (△ on 3rd, ♧ on 5th)

LOHPOA

#2 [ ][ ][ ][ ][ ][ ] (◇ on 1st)

REGORC

#3 [ ][ ][ ][ ][ ][ ] (☆ on 1st, △ on 2nd, △ on 6th)

RGEILB

#4 [ ][ ][ ][ ][ ][ ] (☆ on 1st, △ on 3rd)

ERWNYI

#5 [ ][ ][ ][ ][ ][ ] (△ on 5th, ⊛ on 6th)

SWDOYR

#6 [ ][ ][ ][ ][ ][ ] (△ on 2nd, ⊛ on 6th)

UHMENA

#7 [ ][ ][ ][ ][ ][ ] (◇ on 1st, ♧ on 2nd, □ on 3rd)

ETHNDU

#8 [ ][ ][ ][ ][ ][ ] (◇ on 1st, ♧ on 2nd)

BERAMK

#9 [ ][ ][ ][ ][ ][ ] (□ on 2nd, △ on 5th)

PAT SAJAK'S GAMES & Puzzles # 60

FEATURING PAT'S PATENT PENDING

CODE LETTER SCRAMBLES

MEFLYS

#1 | | ♡ | □ | | △ | ♣ |

LEPTLE

#2 | | | △ | △ | | |

LRYEAR

#3 | | ◇ | | | △ | ♡ |

HOUNKO

#4 | ☆ | | ○ | | | |

RCUVYS

#5 | □ | | ☆ | | | ♡ |

NOFRUF

#6 | | ☆ | | | ♣ | ♣ |

ARLOME

#7 | | | | ◇ | △ | |

LOHUGS

#8 | □ | △ | | ☆ | | ○ |

FUNIPF

#9 | | ☆ | ♣ | ♣ | | |

PAT SAJAK'S

GAMES & Puzzles #61

FEATURING PAT'S PATENT PENDING

CODE LETTER SCRAMBLES

#1 B Y M L S O

	☆	♧			○

#2 O W T R N H

	□				

#3 D E I M E P

♡	♧	◇			

#4 L E F E Y R

				○	☆

#5 T O C O N T

△					

#6 T X F I E A

	♡				

#7 N U H A E M

□		♧			

#8 L O D P Y E

		◇	○		☆

#9 B C A Y R B

△					☆

PAT SAJAK'S

GAMES & Puzzles # 62

FEATURING PAT'S PATENT PENDING

CODE LETTER SCRAMBLES

VTELEW

#1 | ♡ | | | △ | □ | |

OJURIN

#2 | | ♧ | | ◇ | | |

CIARCT

#3 | | | | ♡ | ◇ | |

RICGYN

#4 | | | | ◇ | | |

KESIOM

#5 | | | | ◇ | ☆ | |

CETKOL

#6 | △ | | | | | ♡ |

AMYEMH

#7 | ☆ | | | | | ☆ |

VREETR

#8 | | | □ | | | ♡ |

NRUYUL

#9 | ♧ | | | ♧ | △ | |

PAT SAJAK'S

GAMES & Puzzles #63

FEATURING PAT'S PATENT PENDING

CODE LETTER SCRAMBLES

#1 HESLAV

#2 ESILVW

#3 JEERST

#4 GHAUNT

#5 DECLOK

#6 SHOBIK

#7 BASORI

#8 MOITAC

#9 KLYEEM

PAT SAJAK'S

GAMES & Puzzles

#64

FEATURING PAT'S PATENT PENDING

CODE LETTER SCRAMBLES

CHABER

#1

	⊛				☆

PLAGOL

#2

◇					

FLURAG

#3

♡	⊛	□	◇		

NERZAB

#4

	⊛				

WAFELD

#5

♡					

ZEEFER

#6

♡	⊛				

SHRUGE

#7

◇	□		☆		⊛

THRIBG

#8

	⊛		◇	☆	

LAUCAS

#9

			□		

PAT SAJAK'S

GAMES & Puzzles #65

FEATURING PAT'S PATENT PENDING

CODE LETTER SCRAMBLES

KESNNU

#1 | | | △ | ☆ | | △

ITVIMC

#2 | | | | | | ♡

TAGUEO

#3 | | | | ♣ | |

NIPCCI

#4 | | | | △ | |

NSGVIA

#5 | | ♣ | | | △ |

TESFYA

#6 | | ♣ | | | |

AECBNO

#7 | | | ♣ | | | △

UMAOTN

#8 | ♣ | ♡ | | | △ |

HSKRNU

#9 | | | | | △ | ☆

PAT SAJAK'S

GAMES & Puzzles #66

FEATURING PAT'S PATENT PENDING

CODE LETTER SCRAMBLES

SIEVTN

#1 ☐ △ ☐ ☐ ☐ ◇

CONVEI

#2 △ ☐ ☐ ☐ ☐ ☐

COETBJ

#3 ☐ ☆ ☐ ☐ ☐ ◇

NXBIGO

#4 ☆ ☐ ☐ ☐ △ ☐

NAULNA

#5 ☐ △ △ ☐ ☐ ☐

CNBOOR

#6 ☆ ☐ ☐ △ ☐ ☐

CIEBRK

#7 ☆ ☐ ☐ ☐ ☐ ☐

PRTYOH

#8 ◇ ☐ ☐ ☐ ☐ ☐

VNIEIT

#9 ☐ △ ☐ ☐ ◇ ☐

PAT SAJAK'S

GAMES & Puzzles #67

FEATURING PAT'S PATENT PENDING

CODE LETTER SCRAMBLES

OLGLNA

#1 ◇ (box 2)

UPIRTR

#2 △ (box 6)

AITNNF

#3 △ (box 6)

CRMTIE

#4 △ (box 3), ☆ (box 6)

OGLNBO

#5 ♧ (box 2), ◇ (box 6)

CSOREC

#6 ☆ (box 3), ☆ (box 4)

SBELHU

#7 ♧ (box 1)

NROERC

#8 ☆ (box 1)

ABTOYN

#9 ♧ (box 1), △ (box 3)

PAT SAJAK'S

GAMES & Puzzles #68

FEATURING PAT'S PATENT PENDING

CODE LETTER SCRAMBLES

SORCEA

#1

GEARTT

#2

KORNEB

#3

TTEELR

#4

LICELO

#5

TUNMAU

#6

BEARRL

#7

TOKEPC

#8

RTETBE

#9

PAT SAJAK'S

GAMES & Puzzles #69

FEATURING PAT'S PATENT PENDING

CODE LETTER SCRAMBLES

GSSINA

#1

TUBESO

#2

LOMNUC

#3

XTRAIM

#4

TNITEK

#5

PISMHR

#6

GLGJEU

#7

IDOSUT

#8

ELATRE

#9

PAT SAJAK'S

GAMES & Puzzles #70

FEATURING PAT'S PATENT PENDING

CODE LETTER SCRAMBLES

#1 KLCUEB

△	♧	☆			

#2 TRUEBT

△	♧				♡

#3 HNTRCE

	♡			☆	

#4 URDRDE

♡	♧				♡

#5 TEETRB

△					♡

#6 ETHRET

					♡

#7 RIAWDZ

	◇			♡	

#8 SUREPU

	♧	♡		♧	

#9 MICOAT

				◇	☆

PAT SAJAK'S

GAMES & Puzzles #71

FEATURING PAT'S PATENT PENDING

CODE LETTER SCRAMBLES

SANETB

#1

TNESVI

#2

RIVEGE

#3

LOCOSH

#4

RPEPIZ

#5

HEALIN

#6

RINFUA

#7

GROANE

#8

LTULEB

#9

PAT SAJAK'S

GAMES & Puzzles

72

FEATURING PAT'S PATENT PENDING

CODE LETTER SCRAMBLES

TRIGTY

#1 ☐☆ ☐△ ☐ ☐ ☐ ☐○

BABYLF

#2 ☐ ☐♧ ☐ ☐ ☐ ☐○

TIEING

#3 ☐ ☐☆ ☐ ☐ ☐ ☐

EMOLYH

#4 ☐ ☐□ ☐ ☐ ☐♧ ☐○

GFNAHA

#5 ☐ ☐ ☐☆ ☐ ☐ ☐

UQORIL

☐♧ ☐ ☐ ☐ ☐□ ☐△

GEARUR

☐ ☐△ ☐☆ ☐ ☐ ☐△

SLYRIG

☐☆ ☐△ ☐ ☐ ☐♧ ☐○

NRAGHA

☐ ☐ ☐ ☐☆ ☐ ☐△

PAT SAJAK'S

GAMES & Puzzles #73

FEATURING PAT'S PATENT PENDING

CODE LETTER SCRAMBLES

BDLAKE

#1

☆		△			◇

BEEMML

#2

	○	☆	△		○

DROHIR

#3

♧					◇

BRUUNA

#4

		☆			

MEEDAN

#5

◇		○			

EMXUEH

#6

		♧		○	

BAAMSL

#7

☆		△			○

SHAMBU

#8

	○	☆			♧

BLUMHE

#9

♧		○	☆	△	

PAT SAJAK'S

GAMES & Puzzles #74

FEATURING PAT'S PATENT PENDING

CODE LETTER SCRAMBLES

CIMOAT

#1 | | | | | △ | |

DEERBN

#2 | ☆ | | | ♧ | | |

REALMO

#3 | △ | | | | | |

ROAMCL

#4 | | | | △ | | |

DRYBOW

#5 | ☆ | | | | | ♧ |

DAMESK

#6 | △ | | | ○ | | ♧ |

SHAMBU

#7 | | △ | ☆ | | | |

LIBRED

#8 | ☆ | | | ♧ | | |

NAKEWA

#9 | | | | ○ | | |

PAT SAJAK'S

GAMES & Puzzles #75

FEATURING PAT'S PATENT PENDING

CODE LETTER SCRAMBLES

TEAVIA

#1

GETAOU

#2

ZEWEEH

#3

LEWEVT

#4

VAINGH

#5

DICLAP

#6

CIITMV

#7

VORENP

#8

PEIPRZ

#9

PAT SAJAK'S

GAMES & Puzzles #76

FEATURING PAT'S PATENT PENDING

CODE LETTER SCRAMBLES

OLTJSE

#1 ☐ ☐ ☐☆ ☐◇ ☐□ ☐

VIEWSL

#2 ☐☆ ☐ ☐ ☐ ☐ ☐□

SHIPIM

#3 ☐ ☐ ☐ ☐ ☐☆ ☐♧

ELSEVH

#4 ☐☆ ☐♧ ☐ ☐□ ☐ ☐

LOSTIN

#5 ☐◇ ☐ ☐ ☐☆ ☐ ☐□

AHRIVS

#6 ☐ ☐ ☐ ☐ ☐☆ ☐♧

CSOTEK

#7 ☐☆ ☐ ☐ ☐ ☐ ☐◇

TRIPYU

#8 ☐ ☐ ☐ ☐ ☐◇ ☐

AILOJV

#9 ☐ ☐ ☐ ☐ ☐ ☐□

PAT SAJAK'S

GAMES & Puzzles

77

FEATURING PAT'S PATENT PENDING

CODE LETTER SCRAMBLES

RVIRED

#1

□	♡				♡

NOYANE

#2

	♣	⊛		♣	

SLYGIN

#3

		♣		△	⊛

YENRZF

#4

	♡		♣		⊛

GLAREY

#5

	♡		⊛	△	

LAYTEN

#6

♣				△	⊛

BLIRGE

#7

		♡			△

TOCKED

#8

□					

USJOOY

#9

		⊛			

PAT SAJAK'S

GAMES & Puzzles #78

FEATURING PAT'S PATENT PENDING

CODE LETTER SCRAMBLES

PYGONS

#1

			♧	☆	

RURAGE

#2

	△	☆			△

BRIBEG

#3

☆					△

BERRUG

#4

		△	☆		△

GUMENT

#5

♧					☆

GLYCER

#6

			△	☆	

GANTEE

#7

♧		☆			

IMAGIN

#8

				♧	☆

LIGYHH

#9

		☆			

PAT SAJAK'S

GAMES & Puzzles #79

FEATURING PAT'S PATENT PENDING

CODE LETTER SCRAMBLES

MSRHIP

#1 | ♧ | | | | | |

HILSDE

#2 | ♧ | | | | | ♡ |

FPOTIR

#3 | | | | △ | | ⊛ |

LARFEF

#4 | | | △ | △ | | |

RYOPOD

#5 | ♡ | | | | | □ |

VREETR

#6 | | | ◇ | | | ⊛ |

VSYROA

#7 | ♧ | | ◇ | | | □ |

SEEFTW

#8 | △ | | | | ♧ | ⊛ |

WRODYS

#9 | ♡ | | | | ♧ | □ |

PAT SAJAK'S

GAMES & Puzzles #80

FEATURING PAT'S PATENT PENDING

CODE LETTER SCRAMBLES

YGOVRO

#1

♣				⊛	

FETEDC

#2

				♡	◇

HNTGIK

#3

△		□	♣		◇

OCGURA

#4

♡			♣		

HGELNT

#5

			♣	◇	

INILCC

#6

♡		□		□	♡

TIKENT

#7

△	□	◇	◇		

TRGHWO

#8

♣				◇	

VINDEI

#9

	□	⊛	□		

PAT SAJAK'S

GAMES & Puzzles #81

FEATURING PAT'S PATENT PENDING

CODE LETTER SCRAMBLES

DFELID

#1 | | | | | |

VSLAIH

#2 | | | | | |

LEORLN

#3 | | | | | |

FEOTRF

#4 | | | | | |

CIMOEN

#5 | | | | | |

SISNIT

#6 | | | | | |

CFEIKL

#7 | | | | | |

ATGREH

#8 | | | | | |

TGLNHE

#9 | | | | | |

PAT SAJAK'S

GAMES & Puzzles #82

FEATURING PAT'S PATENT PENDING

CODE LETTER SCRAMBLES

DPLAED

#1 | ♧ | △ | | | | ◇ |

TTEOPN

#2 | ♧ | ⊛ | | ◇ | □ | |

ELOLWF

#3 | | ◇ | | | ⊛ | |

RILTEP

#4 | | | | ♧ | | ◇ |

BENMRU

#5 | □ | | | | ◇ | |

PNEEWH

#6 | □ | ◇ | ♧ | | ◇ | |

AUTEPC

#7 | | ◇ | △ | | | ♧ |

KPCETA

#8 | ♧ | △ | | ♡ | ◇ | |

CTSEHK

#9 | | ♡ | ◇ | | | |

PAT SAJAK'S

GAMES & Puzzles

83

FEATURING PAT'S PATENT PENDING

CODE LETTER SCRAMBLES

MUVLEO

#1

WTRNHO

#2

RWTYOH

#3

DAIECV

#4

AANULN

#5

RTNATY

#6

TWNDAE

#7

CIEODV

#8

MRTUAA

#9

PAT SAJAK'S

GAMES & Puzzles #84

FEATURING PAT'S PATENT PENDING

CODE LETTER SCRAMBLES

DABINT

#1 | | ♡ | | | □ | ⊛ |

YAOENN

#2 | ♡ | | ♧ | ◇ | | |

GIMENL

#3 | △ | □ | | | | |

TAOFRM

#4 | | ◇ | | △ | ♡ | ⊛ |

TCAYTH

#5 | | | ♡ | ⊛ | ⊛ | ♧ |

ANOCNN

#6 | | ♡ | | | ◇ | |

GMVNIO

#7 | △ | ◇ | | □ | | |

BLMEFU

#8 | | | △ | | | |

GNAEYC

#9 | ♡ | | | | | ♧ |

PAT SAJAK'S

GAMES & Puzzles

85

FEATURING PAT'S PATENT PENDING

CODE LETTER SCRAMBLES

#1 RPULEP

#2 AAIFRS

#3 DSEMOT

#4 ERZBYE

#5 CUBELK

#6 KEOTCR

#7 SREUEF

#8 LDPEDU

#9 STMYOL

PAT SAJAK'S

GAMES & Puzzles #86

FEATURING PAT'S PATENT PENDING

CODE LETTER SCRAMBLES

RUBYLR

#1

BELEMM

#2

NFOYLD

#3

RTPEYT

#4

LDCUDE

#5

NTCUYO

#6

YOOECT

#7

RSEUEN

#8

TYABON

#9

PAT SAJAK'S

GAMES & Puzzles

87

FEATURING PAT'S PATENT PENDING

CODE LETTER SCRAMBLES

UNRREN

#1 [ ][ ][♣][◇][◇][ ][ ]

SGIPSO

#2 [ ][ ][ ][ ][ ][△]

NAPRCE

#3 [△][ ][ ][◇][ ][ ]

PGUYMR

#4 [ ][ ][♣][ ][△][♡]

UPCLTS

#5 [ ][ ][♣][□][△][⊛]

PAHENP

#6 [ ][ ][△][△][ ][◇]

RASLYA

#7 [ ][ ][□][ ][ ][♡]

TVRREE

#8 [ ][ ][ ][ ][ ][⊛]

CPIAYR

#9 [△][ ][ ][ ][ ][♡]

PAT SAJAK'S

GAMES & Puzzles #88

FEATURING PAT'S PATENT PENDING

CODE LETTER SCRAMBLES

CGNEAL

#1 ♧ _ _ _ _ _

FUIMNF

#2 ◇ _ _ _ ⊛ _

SLIHAV

#3 _ _ △ ⊛ _ _

KNINPA

#4 _ _ _ ♡ ⊛ _

RTPYAS

#5 _ _ _ _ □ _

ENMARN

#6 ◇ _ _ _ _ □

ELUMBM

#7 ◇ _ ◇ _ _ _

TELEKT

#8 ♡ _ _ _ _ _

VOEGNR

#9 ♧ _ △ _ □ _

PAT SAJAK'S

GAMES & Puzzles

89

FEATURING PAT'S PATENT PENDING

CODE LETTER SCRAMBLES

SOPOEP

#1 ☐ ☐♣ ☐♣ ☐ ☐ ☐

DOSAWH

#2 ☐ ☐ ☐△ ☐ ☐ ☐◇

ASIORL

#3 ☐ ☐△ ☐ ☐ ☐ ☐

CPUIPK

#4 ☐♣ ☐ ☐♡ ☐ ☐ ☐♣

TEEBNA

#5 ☐⊛ ☐ ☐△ ☐ ☐ ☐□

TURAOH

#6 ☐△ ☐ ☐ ☐ ☐ ☐

NOADWR

#7 ☐ ☐□ ☐◇ ☐△ ☐ ☐

EKASTB

#8 ☐⊛ ☐△ ☐ ☐ ☐ ☐

AECIEP

#9 ☐△ ☐♣ ☐ ☐ ☐♡ ☐

PAT SAJAK'S

GAMES & Puzzles #90

FEATURING PAT'S PATENT PENDING

CODE LETTER SCRAMBLES

UNAANL

#1

			♡		♧

SOCOEH

#2

◇					

ALCNUY

#3

♧	♡	◇			△

DIARSU

#4

		□		♡	

SCEOTL

#5

◇	♧				

LTIEPR

#6

				♧	

AODLRL

#7

□		♧	♧		

RRYLUB

#8

	♧	♡			△

FAETFC

#9

				◇	

ANSWERS

HOW DO YOU RANK?

Zero completed = F
One or two completed = D
Three or four completed = C
Five completed = B
Six completed = B+
Seven completed = A-
Eight completed = A
Nine completed = A+

PUZZLE #1	PUZZLE #2	PUZZLE #3	PUZZLE #4	PUZZLE #5
1. UNION	1. PANTS	1. TIDAL	1. KNOWN	1. CARGO
2. YODEL	2. BLUES	2. VODKA	2. SCUBA	2. CONGA
3. WHOLE	3. ABRUPT	3. FLUME	3. MORON	3. PLANT
4. HYBRID	4. AMOUNT	4. NATIVE	4. NORMAL	4. TAVERN
5. BOTHER	5. BRIDLE	5. BITTER	5. MISFIT	5. PIMPLE
6. FABRIC	6. CAMERA	6. FLIMSY	6. BLURRY	6. CLENCH
7. UPHILL	7. JARGON	7. ACTUAL	7. MUTANT	7. PLACID
8. NESTLE	8. CHOSEN	8. MASCOT	8. JUMPER	8. RAISIN
9. ADVERB	9. MANGLE	9. OCTANE	9. POSTAL	9. POCKET

PUZZLE #6	PUZZLE #7	PUZZLE #8	PUZZLE #9	PUZZLE #10
1. PURGE	1. SUNKEN	1. ALOUD	1. MARKET	1. NEGATE
2. PERKY	2. VICTIM	2. LEMUR	2. NUTMEG	2. SWIVEL
3. LATCH	3. OUTAGE	3. CRUMB	3. OUTAGE	3. BARBER
4. COWARD	4. PICNIC	4. GRUMPY	4. HARBOR	4. JOINED
5. JALOPY	5. SAVING	5. FOUGHT	5. HOPPER	5. GOVERN
6. VANISH	6. SAFETY	6. EXTENT	6. REFUND	6. PETITE
7. PUNCHY	7. BEACON	7. ENRICH	7. HELMET	7. NUDIST
8. CREEPY	8. AMOUNT	8. HAPPEN	8. REFUSE	8. PIGLET
9. POTATO	9. SHRUNK	9. GUSHER	9. HERBAL	9. PERSON

PUZZLE #11	PUZZLE #12	PUZZLE #13	PUZZLE #14	PUZZLE #15
1. PURPLE	1. BEDPAN	1. CELERY	1. MYSTIC	1. BOGGLE
2. PHOBIA	2. ASSESS	2. UNLOCK	2. ALLIES	2. IMPUGN
3. INDOOR	3. DAINTY	3. THRONG	3. CARHOP	3. FRIGHT
4. DECEIT	4. FRUITY	4. RADIUM	4. BIOPSY	4. FOUGHT
5. TUMBLE	5. MUFFIN	5. TATTLE	5. COGNAC	5. MARROW
6. TYRANT	6. JOYOUS	6. SHERRY	6. APLOMB	6. KNIGHT
7. WALLOP	7. QUEASY	7. OCELOT	7. BUNGLE	7. GAGGED
8. DEFEAT	8. UNWIND	8. WICKET	8. ENGULF	8. FOREGO
9. VERBAL	9. SNAZZY	9. THORNY	9. AMOEBA	9. HACKER

ANSWERS

PUZZLE #16
1. BARRED
2. CELERY
3. ANKLET
4. BOOKIE
5. CRAGGY
6. DORMER
7. AWAKEN
8. BOBBIN
9. CODDLE

PUZZLE #17
1. DOTTED
2. ITALIC
3. FEISTY
4. HIGHLY
5. INLAND
6. GUFFAW
7. EVENLY
8. JAILER
9. FRIZZY

PUZZLE #18
1. HUMANE
2. LIQUOR
3. LIKING
4. METTLE
5. SIESTA
6. PRANCE
7. MENTOR
8. HUSHED
9. JURIST

PUZZLE #19
1. NUTMEG
2. OCTANE
3. PURPLE
4. RESUME
5. GAZEBO
6. FRIGHT
7. FOURTH
8. CRUNCH
9. DEPLOY

PUZZLE #20
1. ALLUDE
2. BACKER
3. CATNAP
4. CACKLE
5. FLINCH
6. PURITY
7. CRYING
8. GRAVEL
9. COLLIE

PUZZLE #21
1. RAVISH
2. PLUCKY
3. THROWN
4. INFECT
5. GIVING
6 JALOPY
7. GIRDER
8. RENOWN
9. ACCOST

PUZZLE #22
1 PUPPET
2. SPLICE
3. SHROUD
4. MATTED
5. REVOLT
6. SALMON
7. ORPHAN
8. MEMOIR
9. LIMBER

PUZZLE #23
1. ARCHED
2. WHITEN
3. BRAWNY
4. WOODEN
5. CAMPER
6. BUZZER
7. TIPTOE
8. ARGUED
9. WITHER

PUZZLE #24
1. DETACH
2. BROGUE
3. FRACAS
4. CROUCH
5. AMPERE
6. CLERGY
7. AVIATE
8. CINDER
9. DIVEST

PUZZLE #25
1. MENTOR
2. SQUIRM
3. WINERY
4. AMOUNT
5. SALOON
6. RUMPUS
7. MELTED
8. BALSAM
9. SEDUCE

PUZZLE #26
1. PROVEN
2. WHEEZE
3. PIMPLE
4. TOUPEE
5. APPOSE
6. TENPIN
7. PAPAYA
8. WRETCH
9. ANYWAY

PUZZLE #27
1. HYBRID
2. AVIDLY
3. BUSBOY
4. ANYONE
5. DAMAGE
6. PAYDAY
7. DEPLOY
8. AFFORD
9. AGENCY

PUZZLE #28
1. CHANGE
2. BECOME
3. WOODEN
4. RANDOM
5. LONELY
6. SHABBY
7. CRANKY
8 AROUND
9. CHUBBY

PUZZLE #29
1. LENGTH
2. NUMBER
3. SCROLL
4. HUMBLE
5. SHADOW
6. LAGOON
7. HERMIT
8. LEGACY
9.NOVICE

PUZZLE #30
1. WEEKLY
2. STRESS
3. LOUDLY
4. LOCKER
5. PRETTY
6. PEACHY
7. GALLEY
8. MITTEN
9. FAMILY

PUZZLE #31
1. BARREL
2. PERMIT
3. OUTFIT
4. CHURCH
5. CLEVER
6. LETTER
7. FORMAL
8. LOCKED
9. ROLLER

PUZZLE #32
1. BRUTAL
2. GUTTER
3. BEAGLE
4. LESSON
5. BANDIT
6. JACKAL
7. PIGLET
8. RUBBER
9. FIZZLE

PUZZLE #33
1. PERSON
2. DIVIDE
3. TOUCAN
4. OSPREY
5. GALLOP
6. PEPPER
7. COYOTE
8. STRESS
9. CHOOSE

PUZZLE #34
1. TREATY
2. LIVING
3. WRENCH
4. METHOD
5. DEBATE
6. BEAVER
7. THEORY
8. DRIVEN
9. SHIELD

PUZZLE #35
1. ABRUPT
2. FORMAL
3. FACTOR
4. WEASEL
5. LIZARD
6. APOLLO
7. WALRUS
8. CHANCE
9. SALUTE

ANSWERS

PUZZLE #36
1. DEFECT
2. INVADE
3. BOBCAT
4. MONKEY
5. FINISH
6. GARAGE
7. BACKED
8. TURKEY
9. BUBBLE

PUZZLE #37
1. HAGGLE
2. STUPID
3. FINITE
4. RABBIT
5. JACKET
6. CONVEX
7. BALLET
8. SCHEME
9. ACTUAL

PUZZLE #38
1. SHRINK
2. HOLLOW
3. BEHAVE
4. BAFFLE
5. KETTLE
6. NOZZLE
7. MAKING
8. FRIGHT
9. KNIGHT

PUZZLE #39
1. FREEZE
2. FALTER
3. SMUDGE
4. PLEDGE
5. MOTHER
6. NAPKIN
7. MELLOW
8. COMBAT
9. CANNON

PUZZLE #40
1. JOYOUS
2. ACHING
3. ATTACK
4. HAMMER
5. FATHOM
6. CUDDLE
7. POLICE
8. SHIFTY
9. ACTION

PUZZLE #41
1. CLOUDY
2. SUMMON
3. IMPACT
4. IMPEDE
5. UNWIND
6. TRENCH
7. MUSTER
8. UPHILL
9. ORPHAN

PUZZLE #42
1. DEFEAT
2. ANYONE
3. ACCEPT
4. INVITE
5. OBJECT
6. MINING
7. OFFEND
8. UNLESS
9. EXCESS

PUZZLE #43
1. INJURY
2. ACCUSE
3. ONWARD
4. IGNITE
5. CACTUS
6. UNEVEN
7. ALWAYS
8. OCTANE
9. OBLONG

PUZZLE #44
1. MISSUS
2. AMPERE
3. JALOPY
4. MARROW
5. CAMPER
6. CLUMPY
7. MUSLIN
8. PUNCHY
9. RUMPUS

PUZZLE #45
1. SQUIRM
2. ADROIT
3. CRAWLY
4. EQUATE
5. SEQUEL
6. TIDBIT
7. BISQUE
8. SCANTY
9. ABDUCT

PUZZLE #46
1. MARKET
2. ANKLET
3. DARKLY
4. HACKER
5. AVERSE
6. KILLER
7. EUREKA
8. BICKER
9. SHRUNK

PUZZLE #47
1. TOPPLE
2. ROTARY
3. WITHAL
4. THRONG
5. SAFETY
6. STYMIE
7. UNTOLD
8. SYNTAX
9. WINERY

PUZZLE #48
1. DOSAGE
2. ARGYLE
3. DEVOUR
4. TRIBAL
5. DAINTY
6. BIOPSY
7. BREACH
8. ENGULF
9. WIRING

PUZZLE #49
1. COFFIN
2. FACIAL
3. BEACON
4. DEFECT
5. FRISKY
6. SHIFTY
7. BISECT
8. COOKIE
9. ETHNIC

PUZZLE #50
1. BURGER
2. HOOPLA
3. SADDLE
4. POSTAL
5. FLINCH
6. LOAFER
7. TIDING
8. APLOMB
9. SLUDGE

PUZZLE #51
1. ANNUAL
2. FENCED
3. BLANCH
4. CARHOP
5. CLUMPY
6. DEFTLY
7. BOLERO
8. AFLAME
9. CAMPER

PUZZLE #52
1. CREASE
2. BOUNCY
3. ENSURE
4. DRAFTY
5. HAGGLE
6. ARCHED
7. WINERY
8. CAVORT
9. GRAINY

PUZZLE #53
1. JAILER
2. SEDUCE
3. MAGPIE
4. DEPOSE
5. CLIMAX
6. PRANCE
7. INLAND
8. ABDUCT
9. NESTLE

PUZZLE #54
1. DIVEST
2. CHERUB
3. SLOUGH
4. NUDIST
5. HERBAL
6. RADIUM
7. TEACUP
8. DERIVE
9. WORKED

PUZZLE #55
1. ARCHED
2. FRUITY
3. BISQUE
4. MARKED
5. CALLUS
6. APLOMB
7. SNEAKY
8. HACKLE
9. ESKIMO

ANSWERS

PUZZLE #56
1. GROCER
2. FRUGAL
3. LIMBER
4. BRIDLE
5. BECOME
6. KENNEL
7. CURSED
8. DETAIL
9. INFORM

PUZZLE #57
1. MERGE
2. HILLY
3. GROVE
4. EXHALE
5. HANGAR
6. GRAVEL
7. VISUAL
8. FOURTH
9. GAZEBO

PUZZLE #58
1. ALPHA
2. HOARD
3. LOCAL
4. WEIGHT
5. FICKLE
6. SAVAGE
7. WIRING
8. WRENCH
9. AIRWAY

PUZZLE #59
1. VERSUS
2. HOOPLA
3. GROCER
4. GERBIL
5. WINERY
6. DROWSY
7. HUMANE
8. HUNTED
9. EMBARK

PUZZLE #60
1. MYSELF
2. PELLET
3. RARELY
4. UNHOOK
5. SCURVY
6. RUNOFF
7. MORALE
8. SLOUGH
9. PUFFIN

PUZZLE #61
1. SYMBOL
2. THROWN
3. IMPEDE
4. FREELY
5. COTTON
6. FIXATE
7. HUMANE
8. DEPLOY
9. CRABBY

PUZZLE #62
1. TWELVE
2. JUNIOR
3. ARCTIC
4. CRYING
5. ESKIMO
6. LOCKET
7. MAYHEM
8. REVERT
9. UNRULY

PUZZLE #63
1. HALVES
2. SWIVEL
3. JESTER
4. NAUGHT
5. LOCKED
6. KIBOSH
7. ISOBAR
8. ATOMIC
9. MEEKLY

PUZZLE #64
1. BREACH
2. GALLOP
3. FRUGAL
4. BRAZEN
5. FLAWED
6. FREEZE
7. GUSHER
8. BRIGHT
9. CASUAL

PUZZLE #65
1. SUNKEN
2. VICTIM
3. OUTAGE
4. PICNIC
5. SAVING
6. SAFETY
7. BEACON
8. AMOUNT
9. SHRUNK

PUZZLE #66
1. INVEST
2. NOVICE
3. OBJECT
4. BOXING
5. ANNUAL
6. BRONCO
7. BICKER
8. TROPHY
9. INVITE

PUZZLE #67
1. GALLON
2. IRRUPT
3. INFANT
4. METRIC
5. OBLONG
6. SOCCER
7. BUSHEL
8. CORNER
9. BOTANY

PUZZLE #68
1. COARSE
2. TARGET
3. BROKEN
4. LETTER
5. COLLIE
6. AUTUMN
7. BARREL
8. POCKET
9. BETTER

PUZZLE #69
1. ASSIGN
2. OBTUSE
3. COLUMN
4. MATRIX
5. KITTEN
6. SHRIMP
7. JUGGLE
8. STUDIO
9. RELATE

PUZZLE #70
1. BUCKLE
2. BUTTER
3. TRENCH
4. RUDDER
5. BETTER
6. TETHER
7. WIZARD
8. PURSUE
9. ATOMIC

PUZZLE #71
1. ABSENT
2. INVEST
3. GRIEVE
4. SCHOOL
5. ZIPPER
6. INHALE
7. UNFAIR
8. ORANGE
9. BULLET

PUZZLE #72
1. GRITTY
2. FLABBY
3. IGNITE
4. HOMELY
5. AFGHAN
6. LIQUOR
7. ARGUER
8. GRISLY
9. HANGAR

PUZZLE #73
1. BALKED
2. EMBLEM
3. HORRID
4. AUBURN
5. DEMEAN
6. EXHUME
7. BALSAM
8. AMBUSH
9. HUMBLE

PUZZLE #74
1. ATOMIC
2. BENDER
3. MORALE
4. CLAMOR
5. BYWORD
6. MASKED
7. AMBUSH
8. BRIDLE
9. AWAKEN

PUZZLE #75
1. AVIATE
2. OUTAGE
3. WHEEZE
4. TWELVE
5. HAVING
6. PLACID
7. VICTIM
8. PROVEN
9. ZIPPER

ANSWERS

PUZZLE #76
1. JOSTLE
2. SWIVEL
3. IMPISH
4. SHELVE
5. TONSIL
6. RAVISH
7. SOCKET
8. PURITY
9. JOVIAL

PUZZLE #77
1. DRIVER
2. ANYONE
3. SINGLY
4. FRENZY
5. ARGYLE
6. NEATLY
7. GERBIL
8. DOCKET
9. JOYOUS

PUZZLE #78
1. SPONGY
2. ARGUER
3. GIBBER
4. BURGER
5. NUTMEG
6. CLERGY
7. NEGATE
8. AIMING
9. HIGHLY

PUZZLE #79
1. SHRIMP
2. SHIELD
3. PROFIT
4. RAFFLE
5. DROOPY
6. REVERT
7. SAVORY
8. FEWEST
9. DROWSY

PUZZLE #80
1. GROOVY
2. DEFECT
3. KNIGHT
4. COUGAR
5. LENGTH
6. CLINIC
7. KITTEN
8. GROWTH
9. DIVINE

PUZZLE #81
1. FIDDLE
2. LAVISH
3. ENROLL
4. EFFORT
5. INCOME
6. INSIST
7. FICKLE
8. GATHER
9. LENGTH

PUZZLE #82
1. PADDLE
2. POTENT
3. FELLOW
4. TRIPLE
5. NUMBER
6. NEPHEW
7. TEACUP
8. PACKET
9. SKETCH

PUZZLE #83
1. VOLUME
2. THROWN
3. WORTHY
4. ADVICE
5. ANNUAL
6. TYRANT
7. WANTED
8. VOICED
9. TRAUMA

PUZZLE #84
1. BANDIT
2. ANYONE
3. MINGLE
4. FORMAT
5. CHATTY
6. CANNON
7. MOVING
8. FUMBLE
9. AGENCY

PUZZLE #85
1. PURPLE
2. SAFARI
3. MODEST
4. BREEZY
5. BUCKLE
6. ROCKET
7. REFUSE
8. PUDDLE
9. MOSTLY

PUZZLE #86
1. BLURRY
2. EMBLEM
3. FONDLY
4. PRETTY
5. CUDDLE
6. COUNTY
7. COYOTE
8. ENSURE
9. BOTANY

PUZZLE #87
1. RUNNER
2. GOSSIP
3. PRANCE
4. GRUMPY
5. SCULPT
6. HAPPEN
7. SALARY
8. REVERT
9. PIRACY

PUZZLE #88
1. GLANCE
2. MUFFIN
3. LAVISH
4. NAPKIN
5. PASTRY
6. MANNER
7. MUMBLE
8. KETTLE
9. GOVERN

PUZZLE #89
1. OPPOSE
2. SHADOW
3. SAILOR
4. PICKUP
5. BEATEN
6. AUTHOR
7. ONWARD
8. BASKET
9. APIECE

PUZZLE #90
1. ANNUAL
2. CHOOSE
3. LUNACY
4. RADIUS
5. CLOSET
6. TRIPLE
7. DOLLAR
8. BLURRY
9. AFFECT